PSHE & Citizenship
In Action

Year 3

Godfrey Hall

United Kingdom: Folens Publishers, Apex Business Centre, Boscombe Road, Dunstable, LU5 4RL
Email: folens@folens.com

Ireland: Folens Publishers, Greenhills Road, Tallaght, Dublin 24
Email: info@folens.ie

Poland: JUKA, ul. Renesansowa 38, Warsaw 01-905

Editor: Melanie Gray
Layout artist: Suzanne Ward
Illustrations: Mark Stacey
Cover design: Martin Cross

First published 2004 by Folens Limited.

British Library Cataloguing in Publication Data. A catalogue record for this publication is available from the British Library.

ISBN 1 84303 633 9

Contents

Series introduction

This series has been designed to meet the needs of Key Stages 1 and 2. Prepared in conjunction with the QCA Schemes of Work for Citizenship, it also includes sections on personal, social and health education (PSHE).

Citizenship is a central issue in all schools, and a subject which is part and parcel of our everyday lives. Together with PSHE, it provides pupils with the knowledge, skills and understanding that are required for them to lead happy and confident lives.

It is also important that young people grow up to become not only responsible but active and informed citizens.

Issues covered in this series include:
- right and wrong
- rules and laws
- fairness
- healthy living
- being part of the community
- decision making
- conflict and cooperation.

The material and ideas in these books have been designed so that they can be used:
- as part of an ongoing programme
- as a springboard for further investigation
- to support existing schemes.

There are 15 units in each book. Each unit contains three sections, which focus on one issue and include a worksheet to help carry out that task. Each unit provides:
- background information
- learning objectives
- QCA and Curriculum links
- differentiated activities
- follow-up ideas
- three worksheets.

The worksheets have been provided so that they are flexible and can be adapted to the local needs of schools and individual teachers. The activities have also been designed so that they are cross-curricular.

In the later books, pupils are encouraged to work more and more with outside agencies, extending their knowledge of the subject on both a global and a national level.

Many of the activities throughout the series are excellent starting points for projects within the community as well as for links with other schools.

With the development of e-mail and the Internet, pupils are not only able to communicate with others throughout the world; they are also able to carry out intensive research into areas of interest. This allows schools to build partnerships with others. Pupils also have the chance to work closely with their peers. Working with others, investigating sustainable development and developing local and national strategies are all part of this process.

Citizenship and PSHE are important elements of the curriculum because they:
- encourage pupils to take a full part in the life of the school and the community
- provide pupils with the opportunity to become responsible citizens
- link schools with others elsewhere in the world
- provide the ingredients for a healthy lifestyle
- support and promote equal opportunity and respect
- provide a focus for school-based projects
- provide a chance to work on real-life issues
- increase pupils' decision-making opportunities.

① Communication

Background

This unit examines the way in which we use facial expressions and body language to help us when we communicate with each other. It allows the children to experiment with some of the different techniques and acts as a springboard for further work. It is important that the children understand that there are times when we can express our feelings without the use of words.

Learning Objectives

Activities in this unit will allow children to:
- be able to express their opinions with confidence
- speak clearly
- increase their understanding of the importance of body language.

QCA/Curriculum links: QCA Unit 1 • Worksheet 1 links with English, Science and Design & Technology • Worksheet 2 links with English • Worksheet 3 links with English and Science.

ACTIVITIES

Worksheet 1 Keeping in touch

Starting points: Explain to the children that they will be making a tube telephone to use in developing the art of sending messages. They will need two funnels and a length of plastic tubing about ten metres long.

Main activity: The children should make a tube telephone, which can be used to communicate with each other. They will then be able to experiment with pitch, loudness and tone of voice. It will also provide a chance to discuss what makes a good message.

Simplified activity: The children should make a tube telephone and use it to send messages to each other.

Challenge: Ask the children to consider what might be missing when we send a message like this, e.g. facial expressions and body language.

Worksheet 2 Face it

Starting points: Explain to the children that they will investigate some of the facial expressions we might use when we communicate with each other.

Main activity: The children could talk about the importance of using facial expressions to convey how they feel. Then they should look at the faces on the

worksheet. How do expressions help in understanding what people are saying to each other?

Simplified activity: Ask the children to look at the faces on the worksheet. What are the people feeling in these pictures?

Challenge: The children could write a short story about each person illustrated on the worksheet. What has happened to them and why do they feel like they do?

Worksheet 3 Body language

Starting points: Explain to the children that you will be looking at how our body language helps in communication. How can we use our body to show that we are happy or sad?

Main activity: The children should look at the illustration on the worksheet. What has happened to bring about this situation? Can they tell how the people feel from their body language? What do they think might happen next?

Simplified activity: Ask the children what has happened to bring about this situation and how it could be sorted out.

Challenge: The children could work out three different endings to the problem in the picture.

Plenary

In pairs, ask the children to mime to their partner something that has happened to them during the day. Stress the importance of facial expressions and body language. Ask a group of children to tell a popular story using mime, e.g. Little Red Riding Hood, to the rest of the class.

PSHE & Citizenship in Action: Year 3

Keeping in touch

 You are going to make a tube telephone.

- **Push the funnels into the two ends of the tube.**

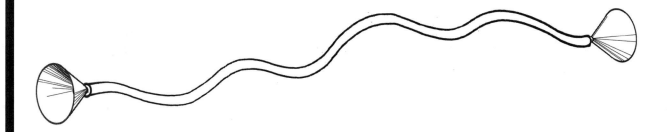

- **Ask a friend to take one end of the telephone round a corner.**
- **Quietly pass a message to them down the telephone. Ask them to write it down.**
- **Take turns in sending messages.**

1. **a.** Was it easy to understand the messages?

   _____

   b. Explain why.

   _____

2. What difference does it make if you change the pitch of your voice?

   _____

3. What was missing from the messages?

   _____

4. How could you improve your telephone messaging service?

   _____

Face it

**Look at the pictures below.
How do these people feel? Write your ideas in the clouds.
What might have happened to them to make them feel like this?
Write your answers on the lines.**

Body language

Look at the picture below.

What has happened? How could this problem be sorted out?

_____

_____

_____

_____

_____

_____

_____

_____

_____

_____

_____

_____

② Working together

Background

This unit provides the children with a series of situations where they will be asked to solve a problem. This gives the children experience in working together and understanding the importance of group dynamics. They will use real-life situations and the worksheets involve planning, testing and trialling their ideas.

Learning Objectives

Activities in this unit will allow children to:
- use group skills
- learn how to work with others
- begin to understand the importance of feedback and constructive criticism.

QCA/Curriclum links: QCA Unit 1 • Worksheet 4 links with English, Maths, Art & Design and PE • Worksheet 5 links with English and Maths • Worksheet 6 links with English and Maths.

ACTIVITIES

Worksheet 4 A new game

Starting points: Explain that the children will be developing a new activity for a PE lesson or a game for the playground.

Main activity: The children should look at what takes place in either a PE lesson or during breaktime and work out a new activity that could be devised. They need to explain why their new activity should be introduced.

Simplified activity: The children could draw a series of pictures showing how their game might be played.

Challenge: Ask the children to describe the game in detail in such a way that other children might be able to play it. These instructions should include any equipment required.

Worksheet 5 New instructions

Starting points: Building on Worksheet 4, the children will write a set of instructions and rules on how to play the game. These should be presented in a clear and concise format.

Main activity: The children should prepare a set of instructions and rules to be followed.

Simplified activity: Ask the children to write down five simple rules for their game or activity.

Challenge: The children could prepare two sets of instructions and rules, one for 5- to 7-year-olds and one for 7- to 11-year-olds.

Worksheet 6 Putting it to work

Starting points: The children should explain how the game works and then go through the rules. They should ask several groups of children of different ages to try out the game. In a group situation, discuss ways in which the game could be improved. These changes need to be incorporated into the revised game.

Main activity: The children should use the worksheet to write down any comments/observations from the players after they have played the game.

Simplified activity: The children could watch the game being played and list any problems.

Challenge: Ask the children to rewrite the instructions and rules using the comments made by the players. They could write their revised instructions and rules on a set of cards for use in the school.

Plenary

When this mini project is complete, get the children together and discuss with them any problems they might have encountered. How did they incorporate the comments into their revisions? Were there any major changes that had to be made?

A new game

 Look at what takes place in a PE lesson or during breaktime. Work out a new activity that could be played.

Why do you think a new game is needed?

_____

_____

Draw a set of pictures showing how to play your new game.

Describe how to play your game.

New instructions

Write down a set of instruction and five rules for your new game.

Instructions

Rules

1 _____

2 _____

3 _____

4 _____

5 _____

Putting it to work

 Write down any comments after the players have tried out the game.

Name _____

Comments _____

_____

Name _____

Comments _____

_____

Name _____

Comments _____

_____

Name _____

Comments _____

_____

Name _____

Comments _____

_____

Name _____

Comments _____

_____

③ Decisions

Background

When making a decision it is sometimes necessary to look at alternatives and the consequences. For example, where are you going to cross the road? You may have found a safe place but is there somewhere safer such as a bridge or an underpass? If you use the underpass, are there any other dangers? The children need to consider strategies concerning decision making and also to be able to explain their decisions and why they have made them.

Learning Objectives
Activities in this unit will allow children to:
- look at decision-making strategies
- consider alternatives
- explain the reasons behind their decisions.

QCA/Curriculum links: QCA Unit 2 • Worksheet 7 links with English and Art & Design • Worksheet 8 links with English, Design & Technology, ICT and Art & Design • Worksheet 9 links with English.

ACTIVITIES

Worksheet 7 — Decision making

Starting points: Explain that the children will be looking at ways of creating decision-making diagrams, listing options and what the consequences might be.

Main activity: The children should consider a number of decisions and how they might be addressed. What are the consequences?

Simplified activity: The children could consider what might happen if they do something. How might it affect other people?

Challenge: Ask the children to produce a list of things that might influence the decisions they have made on the worksheet, e.g. a television report, a newspaper article, a conversation with a friend.

Worksheet 8 — Persuading people

Starting points: Explain that the children will be looking at ways television and newspapers try to change our point of view.

Main activity: The children should produce two drawings advertising a product. Each drawing should have an opposing message.

Simplified activity: The children could collect a selection of adverts from magazines and newspapers based on one theme, e.g. cars, clothes. Ask them to look at the methods used to persuade people, such as colour and location.

Challenge: The children could role play two adverts in front of the class. Both must have totally different points of view.

Worksheet 9 — Making a difference

Starting points: Ask the children to consider whether it is possible to change someone's point of view. Discuss some of the things that might change someone's decision to do something.

Main activity: The children should look at the list of decisions and write down something that might happen to change their decision.

Simplified activity: The children could think about decisions that have to be made every day. For example, whether you should brush your teeth or what you should eat for breakfast.

Challenge: Ask the children to design a poster with the title 'Choices'. This could be put up in the class or around the school.

Plenary

Read a story linked with friendship, e.g. the Frog and the Toad. Discuss the importance of friends and how they can sometimes persuade us to do something. Discuss how friends can influence our choices.

Decision making

What might happen if you made the following decisions?

To smoke a cigarette →

To cross the road on a bend →

To steal some sweets from a shop →

To play near a pond →

To drop some litter on the ground →

Persuading people

 Draw two posters. The first one should persuade people to eat sweets. The second one should persuade people not to eat sweets.

Making a difference

 Write down something that might happen to change your mind about these things.

1. What to wear _____

   _____

2. Where to go on holiday _____

   _____

3. What to eat _____

   _____

4. What to watch on television _____

   _____

5. What time to go to bed _____

   _____

6. How much pocket money you should get _____

   _____

7. Which pet to buy _____

   _____

8. What music to listen to _____

   _____

9. Which way to go to school _____

   _____

10. Where to play _____

   _____

(4) Animals

Background

This unit looks at the needs of animals. It examines the role voluntary groups take and the role of local groups. The children should have the chance to discuss what happens to pets when they are hurt and why it is wrong to mistreat them. Just like people, there are laws to protect them. What happens to animals if no one looks after them?

Learning Objectives

Activities in this unit will allow children to:
- learn about the responsibility we have for the care of animals
- examine the role of voluntary charities
- understand that there are laws protecting the welfare of animals.

QCA/Curriclum links: QCA Unit 3 • Worksheet 10 links with English • Worksheet 11 links with English, Science and Geography • Worksheet 12 links with English.

ACTIVITIES

Worksheet 10 Charities

Starting points: Talk about why people volunteer for things and what the job of a charity might be. Discuss local charities that have been set up for the care of animals, e.g. donkey sanctuary, hedgehog hospital. Why were they set up? Ask the children to look at how charities promote kindness, the prevention of cruelty and the welfare of animals.

Main activity: The children should look at the list of animals and write down who might help each animal if they were in need.

Simplified activity: The children could consider how a vet might help a sick animal.

Challenge: The children could investigate one national animal charity, e.g. the RSPCA, finding out how it started and what it does. If there is a local office, ask a representitive to come in and talk about their role.

Worksheet 11 Protecting animals

Starting points: Discuss with the children some of the laws that need to be in place to protect animals from cruelty. Talk about how farm animals need to be looked after. Discuss the kind of things people who work for charities do to see that animals are looked after properly, e.g. regular checks of their living quarters.

Main activity: The children should write down a list of five laws that need to be followed when looking after any type of animal.

Simplified activity: Ask the children to talk about different pets and their needs. What should be done if they become ill?

Challenge: Ask the children to consider what makes for a good pet owner. How can we protect our own animals and those of others? The children could write down why some people would not make good pet owners, e.g. those who are out at work all day or go away a lot.

Worksheet 12 Owning a pet

Starting points: Talk about the kind of pets the children might like to own. Which pets would suit which children?

Main activity: The children should name a pet and write down ten things they would need to do to look after this pet properly.

Simplified activity: The children could write down some of the needs of one pet – this may be an animal that the children own or one that they would like to have.

Challenge: Ask the children to write a story about a 'rescue' pet. Where did it come from and what happened to it after it was rescued?

Plenary

Collect some brochures and leaflets on different animal charities. Pass the leaflets around and discuss what the purposes are of these organisations. What do they do? Which charities might be able to help wild animals, farm animals, pets?

Charities

 Look at this list of animals. Who might help them if they were in need?

Horse _____

Fox _____

Dog _____

Cow _____

Hedgehog _____

Name three local animal charities.

_____

_____

_____

Name three national animal charities.

_____

_____

Protecting animals

Write down five laws that would help protect animals.

Animal laws

1 _____
   _____

2 _____
   _____

3 _____
   _____

4 _____
   _____

5 _____
   _____

Owning a pet

Name a pet and write down ten things you would need to do to look after this pet properly.

My pet

How to look after my pet

1. _____
2. _____
3. _____
4. _____
5. _____
6. _____
7. _____
8. _____
9. _____
10. _____

20

⑤ The police

Background

The object of this unit is to reflect on the purpose of the police and discover more about what they do to prevent crime and how they keep the community safe. This can be achieved by working closely with your local school police liaison officer and the local police station.

Learning Objectives

Activities in this unit will allow children to:
- learn about the role of the police in the local community
- identify the key role of the police
- find out more about how the police go about their job.

QCA/Curriculum links: QCA Unit 4 • Worksheet 13 links with English, Maths, Design & Technology and ICT • Worksheet 14 links with English, Design & Technology, ICT and Art & Design • Worksheet 15 links with English, ICT and Art & Design.

ACTIVITIES

Worksheet 13 Our local police station

Starting points: Arrange for your local school police liaison officer to come in and talk about what happens in a police station or make a visit to your local station. Before the children make the visit, they could prepare a set of questions to ask and a list of things they want to find out.

Main activity: The children should draw a map showing the location of the police station and prepare a set of questions for the visit to the station. These should be based on what the children might see and the people they may meet.

Simplified activity: The children could produce a set of simple questions to be asked.

Challenge: Ask the children to investigate how the police help to keep the community safe. They could produce a leaflet on community safety.

Worksheet 14 The job of the police

Starting points: After a possible visit to a police station, discuss what kind of things the police do. This could involve a number of specialist divisions such as the dog section, CID and the river police. It is important that the children understand the diversity of the work. They could also investigate how the police force started.

Main activity: The children should complete the sentences on the worksheet, which list some of the jobs carried out by the police and specialist divisions.

Simplified activity: The children could draw a picture of one of the jobs carried out by specialist teams, e.g. divers, dogs, river police.

Challenge: Ask the children to produce a poster showing the work of some of the various departments, e.g. horses, dogs, drugs.

Worksheet 15 Stopping crime

Starting points: Talk about how the community and the school can work with the police to help prevent crime, e.g. better streetlights. Ask someone from the local community to come in and talk about how they are working with the police.

Main activity: The children should draw a picture showing some of the ways the local area could be improved, e.g. streetlights, CCTV.

Simplified activity: Ask the children to list some of the ways the area could be improved.

Challenge: The children could make up two plays, one to show show what might happen in an area where there is no contact with the police, and the other where the police and the local community are working together.

Plenary

Make a list of the main functions of the local police station. Talk with the children about how they might co-operate with the police to prevent crime and how the local community can do the same, e.g. neighbourhood watch.

Our local police station

👉 **Draw a map to show where your police station can be found.**

Write a list of questions you can ask on your visit.

The job of the police

Complete these sentences.

1. The police sometimes travel around in _____ .

2. The job of the river police is to _____ .

3. Police dogs are used to _____ .

4. The CID _____ .

5. The police can stop and search people if _____ .

6. Police sometimes ride horses that are used to _____ .

7. You will find the police at football matches _____ .

8. The British Transport Police look after_____ .

9. The police work _____ .

10. Police divers are used to _____ .

Draw a picture of the police at work.

Stopping crime

 Draw a picture showing ways of preventing crime in your area.

⑥ The world we live in

Background

It is important that the children reflect on the rich diverse culture of the UK. They need to consider what their home is like and how it compares with others. Discuss with them what they feel should be included in a home. What are the similarities between their home and those of others in the class? Talk about what kind of things are organised within the community for everyone to take part in.

Learning Objectives

Activities in this unit will allow children to:
■ develop a sense of empathy with the local community
■ consider the views and opinions of others
■ examine similarities and differences.

QCA/Curriculum links: QCA Unit 5 • Worksheet 16 links with English and Art & Design • Worksheet 17 links with English and Geography • Worksheet 18 links with English, ICT and Geography.

ACTIVITIES

Worksheet 16 My home

Starting points: Discuss what makes a 'home'. Is it just a building or do the people who live there matter? What do the children feel like when they are at home? How is it different from being at school? How many of the children have lived in more than one home? Have any lived abroad or elsewhere in the UK?

Main activity: The children should draw a picture of their home, showing it from the inside and the outside.

Simplified activity: The children could draw one room in their home, together with a picture of the outside.

Challenge: Ask the children to write down a list of words that describe the inside and outside of their home. They could go on to describe what it is like.

Worksheet 17 Our community

Starting points: Where do your community meet? Is there a special hall or building? What kind of activities are arranged for the neighbourhood? Discuss social clubs, religious groups and community incentives.

Main activity: The children should list and describe some of the organisations in your area.

Simplified activity: Ask the children to draw a poster advertising one organisation.

Challenge: The children could invent a new club. What would its purpose be and who would it appeal to? How would the children organise it?

Worksheet 18 Things from abroad

Starting points: Bring in a range of items such as food, clothes and objects from various countries or show pictures of them. Ask the children where they might come from. Make a trip to the local supermarket. List where the fruits and vegetables come from.

Main activity: The children should look at the map and mark where the items illustrated have come from. They could then go on to write a letter to a friend.

Simplified activity: Ask the children to colour in the map and say where they think each item comes from.

Challenge: Ask the children to add three more items to the list and mark where they come from on the map.

Plenary

Talk about the possibility of linking up with another school overseas to find out more about where they live. This could be done using the Internet. A good way to start is to contact the Royal Commonwealth Society (www.rcsint.org). Talk about what activities you might be able to do, e.g. exchange items with the other school, chat on the Internet, email pictures of your school.

PSHE & Citizenship in Action: Year 3

My home

 Draw pictures of the inside and outside of your home.

Inside

Words to describe it

Outside

Words to describe it

Our community

 Which organisations provide activities for young and old people in your area?

Make a list below and say what each organisation does.

Organisation	Activities

Do you or your family belong to any of these organisations?

Things from abroad

 Mark on the map where you would find the following things. Write the number for each item.

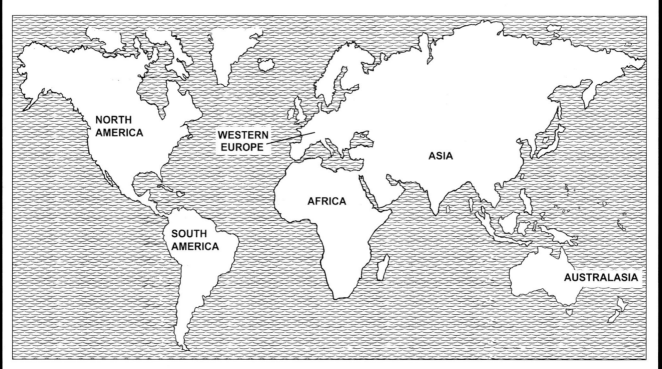

Imagine you are on holiday. Write a letter to a friend back home, describing some of the things you have seen on your holiday.

(7) Our school

Background

While investigating the school grounds, the children should have the opportunity of interviewing people involved in the running of the school and visitors. They will be able to talk to people, find out their views and draw their own conclusions from their discussions. The children will be able to identify their own views and make suggestions for improvements. It will allow them to share ideas and listen to others.

Learning Objectives

Activities in this unit will allow children to:
- record geographical features on a map
- consult with others
- consider their own views and look at various options.

QCA/Curriculum links: QCA Unit 6 • Worksheet 19 links with English, Maths, ICT and Geography • Worksheet 20 links with English and Geography • Worksheet 21 links with English, Maths, Science and Art & Design.

ACTIVITIES

Worksheet 19 Maps

Starting points: The children will take a walk around the school grounds, looking at the physical features and things that have been added, such as benches and litter bins. Talk about how the physical contours of the land and the vegetation could be incorporated into any new changes.

Main activity: The children should draw a map of the exterior of the building and the school grounds showing the existing features.

Simplified activity: The children could colour in red the areas that are used most frequently and green the areas that are used less frequently.

Challenge: Ask the children to make a copy of the map and mark on it any new features they would like to see. Underneath the map they could write a description of these features and say why they would be a good idea.

Worksheet 20 Our school community

Starting points: Discuss how the school grounds are used by different people such as areas used by children, adults and visitors, e.g. delivery drivers.

Main activity: Ask the children to use the questionnaire to find out what their school community thinks of the existing facilities. How might things be improved? They should talk to a cross-section of the school community, e.g. teacher, parent, assistant and visitor.

Simplified activity: In pairs, ask the children to fill in the questionnaire and discuss the results.

Challenge: The children could look at the questionnaires and see if there are any common problems or complaints.

Worksheet 21 The changing seasons

Starting points: This worksheet looks at how the playground and surrounding areas are used at different times of the year. What are the dangers and what issues need to be considered if there were to be any improvements?

Main activity: The children should draw pictures of the playground during the summer and winter.

Simplified activity: The children could complete the drawings and say what is going on in them.

Challenge: Ask the children to consider any improvements. How will these be affected by the change in seasons, e.g. icy paths, falling leaves?

Plenary

Talk about the school map, the questionnaire and the importance of providing a facility that is weatherproof and can be used throughout the year. Discuss any conclusions the children can draw from their answers. What could the next step be?

Maps

Draw a map of your school and the school grounds.

Our school community

 Use copies of this questionnaire to find out what different people think of the facilities at your school.

Name: _____

Job: _____

1. What do you like about the school grounds?

   _____

   _____

2. What you dislike about the school grounds?

   _____

   _____

3. How do you think the school grounds could be improved?

   _____

   _____

4. a. Which part of the grounds is the most attractive?

   _____

   b. Explain why.

   _____

   _____

5. a. What do you think of the play equipment?

   _____

   _____

   b. How could it be improved?

   _____

   _____

The changing seasons

 Draw pictures of the playground in winter and in summer.

Winter

Summer

8 Rights

Background

In this unit the children start to learn about rights and they have the opportunity to consider the importance of trust and honesty. They will learn the difference between wants and needs and recognise the difference between being fair and unfair. They will also be introduced to the concept of responsibility and how they might be able to take this on board.

Learning Objectives

Activities in this unit will allow children to:
- understand the difference between their needs and wants
- recognise what is fair and unfair
- learn about different types of responsibility.

QCA/Curriculum links: QCA Unit 7 • Worksheet 22 links with English, Geography and Art & Design • Worksheet 23 links with English and Art & Design • Worksheet 24 links with English.

ACTIVITIES

Worksheet 22 Wants and needs

Starting points: Talk about what kind of things the children think they might need if they were going to have to live for a week in the desert or in the Arctic. What would they need to survive? If they could only take five things, what would they be?

Main activity: The children will decide which things on the list are 'wants' and which are 'needs'.

Simplified activity: Ask the children to draw some of the things that are 'needs'.

Challenge: The children could write down which things are necessary to keep us alive and which just make our life more comfortable. Which item is the most important thing on the list? Ask them to explain why.

Worksheet 23 Unfair and fair

Starting points: Read a story or nursery rhyme where someone is treated unfairly (a good example is Cinderella). Discuss why the characters in the story were treated in this way. What happens to change the situation?

Main activity: The children should look at the characters on the worksheet. Were they treated fairly or unfairly? Ask them to explain why.

Simplified activity: Ask the children to draw a picture of one of the characters given on the worksheet.

Challenge: The children could consider whether boys and girls are treated in the same way at school and elsewhere. They could then go on to make a list of five things that they think are unfair at school or at home.

Worksheet 24 Being responsible

Starting points: Discuss when the children might need to make a decision and take on responsibility, e.g. looking after a younger brother or sister, taking care of a pet, going shopping, being team captain.

Main activity: The children should consider the five problems given on the worksheet and how they might be resolved.

Simplified activity: Ask the children to draw a picture showing how one of the problems could be resolved.

Challenge: The children could write down how working with someone else might help resolve each of the problems described.

Plenary

Ask the children to get into pairs and work out how they might operate a 'buddy' service in the school, where older children look after younger ones. How could it work? Talk about the responsibilities of the teacher.

Wants and needs

 Look at this list. What do you think you *need* and what do you think you *want*? Put a tick in the right boxes.

	Need	Want
Computer	☐	☐
Food	☐	☐
Television	☐	☐
DVD player	☐	☐
Toys	☐	☐
Bicycle	☐	☐
Ice cream	☐	☐
Lemonade	☐	☐
Camera	☐	☐
Video recorder	☐	☐
Water	☐	☐
Friendship	☐	☐
Shelter	☐	☐
Trainers	☐	☐
Books	☐	☐
Warmth	☐	☐

Unfair and fair

Were these characters treated fairly or unfairly? Explain why.

1. The wolf in Little Red Riding Hood. **Fairly** ☐ **Unfairly** ☐

_____

_____

2. Snow White. **Fairly** ☐ **Unfairly** ☐

_____

_____

3. The giant in Jack and the Beanstalk. **Fairly** ☐ **Unfairly** ☐

_____

_____

4. The tortoise in the Hare and the Tortoise. **Fairly** ☐ **Unfairly** ☐

_____

_____

5. Cinderella. **Fairly** ☐ **Unfairly** ☐

_____

_____

6. Hansel and Gretel. **Fairly** ☐ **Unfairly** ☐

_____

_____

© Folens (copiable page) PSHE & Citizenship in Action: Year 3

Being responsible

**Read the problems below.
What would you do if they happened to you?**

1. You go outside into the playground. The water fountain is not working.

   _____

   _____

   _____

2. You see a new child standing on their own in the playground.

   _____

   _____

   _____

3. There is a fight going on between a boy and a girl outside the classroom.

   _____

   _____

   _____

4. Next door's dog keeps getting through the fence into your garden.

   _____

   _____

   _____

5. Lots of coats have fallen onto the floor in the cloakroom.

   _____

   _____

   _____

⑨ Rules and laws

Background

Children need to learn that rules are there to help us. This can be achieved through discussion and relating the making of rules to their own experiences. Discussion is part of the process, as is debate. This can be stimulated by group sessions and together as a class. The children should be able to make their own suggestions and be open to constructive criticism. Any changes to existing class or school rules should be made through class discussion or a school council, if one exists.

Learning Objectives

Activities in this unit will allow children to:
- learn how important rules and laws are
- find out who makes the laws
- discover what happens if people break them.

QCA/Curriculum links: QCA Unit 8 • Worksheet 25 links with English and PE • Worksheet 26 links with English and History • Worksheet 27 links with English and PE.

ACTIVITIES

Worksheet 25 — Why do we need rules and laws?

Starting points: Discuss the different kinds of rules we have to follow every day in school and elsewhere. Talk about why we have rules, e.g. to help us live together, to be fair, to protect us. Why might a rule need changing? How can this be done?

Main activity: The children should make a list of rules that have to be followed in different circumstances at school and at home.

Simplified activity: The children could colour in red the most important rules in each section.

Challenge: Ask the children to write down a list of games where there is a referee. What do they do? Are they part of a team? Do all sports have referees?

Worksheet 26 — Who makes the laws?

Starting points: Talk about what parliament does. Find out what the children already know. Explain in simple terms what an MP does. Talk about the importance of laws. What would happen if there were no laws? Explain one law in more detail, e.g. the age at which you can drive a car.

Main activity: The children should fill the blanks in the sentences.

Simplified activity: The children could draw a picture of the Houses of Parliament.

Challenge: Ask the children to write a story about a country where there are no laws at all.

Worksheet 27 — Breaking the rules

Starting points: Talk about the main rules or laws that are broken by children. Talk about situations where someone breaks a rule, e.g. at school, in a game, parking a car, crossing the road when the light is red. In pairs, ask the children to role play what might happen.

Main activity: The children should write down what might happen if certain rules or laws are broken.

Simplified activity: The children could write down a list of rules that might have been broken in the classroom.

Challenge: Ask the children to look through local or national newspapers and cut out any examples of rules or laws that have been broken.

Plenary

Make up a class list of ten everyday rules that would help to keep us safe. Have a vote to find out which rules are the three most popular. This activity could be extended to cover more specific areas such as riding a bicycle, walking along the road.

Why do we need rules and laws?

 We need rules and laws to help us to live together and to protect us. Write down three rules for each of these situations.

In the playground

1 _____

_____

2 _____

_____

3 _____

_____

Going to bed

1 _____

_____

2 _____

_____

3 _____

_____

Walking to school

1 _____

_____

2 _____

_____

3 _____

_____

Watching the television at home

1 _____

_____

2 _____

_____

3 _____

_____

38

Who makes the laws?

 Complete these sentences using the words in the box at the bottom.

1. The leader of the government is the _____ _____ .

2. MP stands for _____ _____ _____ .

3. The Houses of Parliament are in _____ .

4. Parliament makes the _____ .

5. The prime minister lives at 10 _____ _____ .

6. The _____ opens parliament every year.

7. There are _____ main political parties.

8. _____ belong to a party.

9. MPs meet at the _____ _____ _____ .

10. Every part of the _____ has its own MP.

---

laws • member of parliament • prime minister • London

Downing Street • monarch • three

MPs • Houses of Parliament • country

Breaking the rules

What might happen to you if you did each of these things?

1. Hit another child in the playground?

_____

_____

2. Crossed the road on a red light?

_____

_____

3. Stole some sweets from a shop?

_____

_____

4. Damaged someone's car on purpose?

_____

_____

5. Tore another child's work off the wall?

_____

_____

6. Threw your plate on the floor at home?

_____

_____

7. Called someone names in class?

_____

_____

8. Kicked another player during a game of football?

_____

_____

9. Rode your bike along the pavement?

_____

_____

10. Shouted at your teacher?

_____

_____

Respect

Background

In this unit the children learn about respecting other people's property, that stealing is wrong and that they need to be responsible for their own actions. They also need to understand that we have a collective responsibility for our neighbourhood.

Learning Objectives

Activities in this unit will allow children to:
- understand that stealing is a crime and consider the consequences
- respect other people's property
- consider the importance of looking after public areas such as parks, town centres and woodlands.

QCA/Curriculum links: QCA Unit 9 • Worksheet 28 links with English • Worksheet 29 links with English and Geography • Worksheet 30 links with English, Maths, Science and Design & Technology.

ACTIVITIES

Worksheet 28   Stealing is wrong

Starting points: Discuss as a class what might happen to someone if they are caught stealing at school, at home or in a shop. How would it affect the victim? Use a simple story or rhyme to bring this out, e.g. the Knave of Hearts who stole the tarts. Talk about why it is wrong to steal.

Main activity: The children should consider what kind of punishment the people shown on the worksheet might receive. What would the victims feel like?

Simplified activity: Ask the children to think about why we should not steal things. They could then write down why it is wrong to steal.

Challenge: The children could consider whether there are any alternatives to punishing the people shown on the worksheet. What makes people want to steal? They could write a short story based on how a victim might feel.

Worksheet 29   A lack of respect

Starting points: Discuss a possible incident at school when everyone is affected, e.g. lots of coats in the cloakroom have been covered in mud. How do the children feel? What do they do? What would they feel like if someone broke into the school grounds and damaged trees and plants?

Main activity: The children should look at the picture on the worksheet and write a story about how this has happened.

Simplified activity: Ask the children to colour in the picture.

Challenge: The children could think about what the consequences of vandalism might be for the whole school. They could write down some ways in which this scenario might have been prevented.

Worksheet 30   Looking after where we live

Starting points: If possible, go for a walk around the local area and identify some of the open spaces that are used for games, walking and sport. Discuss what kind of pleasures people get from these spaces. How might they be affected by vandalism?

Main activity: The children should look at the map on the worksheet, marking on it some of the things that might make the space more attractive and ways in which it could be used by everyone.

Simplified activity: Ask the children to colour in red any areas of the open space that might be vandalised. How might this be prevented?

Challenge: The children could design some vandal-proof litterbins and signs that could be used in your open space.

Plenary

In a group talk about the importance of respecting property and looking after it. Emphasise that public facilities are often used by different people, e.g. young families, older people, the disabled, people with dogs. In pairs, ask them to decide on the punishment to go with certain crimes. These can be written on cards.

PSHE & Citizenship in Action: Year 3

Stealing is wrong

 What kind of punishment might these people get?

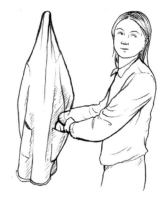

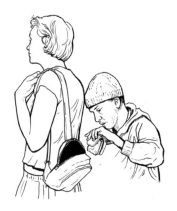

_____
_____
_____
_____
_____
_____
_____
_____
_____
_____
_____
_____
_____
_____
_____
_____
_____
_____
_____
_____
_____
_____

A lack of respect

What has happened here?
Write a story or news report on this event.

_____

_____

_____

_____

_____

_____

_____

_____

_____

_____

_____

_____

Looking after where we live

 This map shows an open space. Make it more interesting by adding a play area and seats. What else could you include?

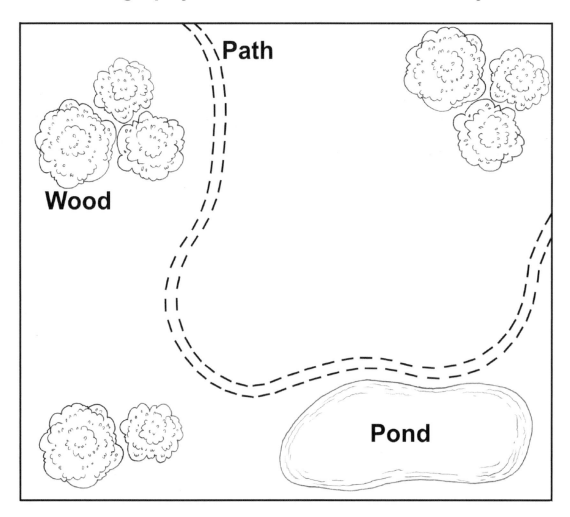

Why have you added these things?

_____

_____

_____

_____

_____

_____

_____

_____

(11) Local democracy

Background

This unit gives the children a chance to investigate their own local community; it allows them to find out where it is located and some of its main features. They will be able to investigate if there are any well-known buildings, people or physical features in the area. The unit also looks at how certain people might represent the community in a variety of issues. Finally, it looks at the role of the mayor.

Learning Objectives

Activities in this unit will allow children to:
■ explore their local community and how it has changed over time
■ find out who represents members of the community
■ discover more about the role of the mayor.

QCA/Curriculum links: QCA Unit 10 • Worksheet 31 links with English, Maths, History and Geography • Worksheet 32 links with English and RE • Worksheet 33 links with English, Design & Technology and Art & Design.

ACTIVITIES

Worksheet 31 Our local community

Starting points: Collect some maps and photographs of your locality now and in the past. Talk about how the area has changed. Discuss any major features, e.g. rivers, bridges, ports. Why might these have an influence on the development of the area?

Main activity: The children should draw a map of the area marking in the main features and any points of interest.

Simplified activity: Ask the children to write down the names of some of the main features, e.g. bridges, rivers.

Challenge: The children could draw a map of the area as they think it might have looked 100 years ago.

Worksheet 32 Who helps us?

Starting points: Ask the children to suggest who might help in the community, e.g. doctor, dentist, police officer. Ask the children who might represent them, e.g. residents' group, local religious leaders, community leaders, local councillors, MP.

Main activity: The children should complete the worksheet by writing down what they think each of the people in the community does.

Simplified activity: Ask the children to write down the names of any of these people in their community.

Challenge: The children could find out who their local MP is and their role. They could write a letter to the MP or the local council, inviting a member into school to talk about their job.

Worksheet 33 The mayor

Starting points: Discuss what the mayor does. How does he or she get the job? Look through local papers and see if there are any pictures of the mayor or councillors at events. Cut them out and make a display. It might also be possible to invite the mayor in to talk about their job.

Main activity: The children should complete the worksheet by writing down some of the things their mayor does, who else helps them in their job, and what special clothes they wear.

Simplified activity: The children could draw a picture of the mayor opening a new building.

Challenge: Ask the children to imagine what it would be like to be mayor for a day, writing down their thoughts and experiences.

Plenary

Ask the children if they have relatives or friends who have lived in the area for a long time. Ask them to come in and talk about any changes that have taken place.

Our local community

Draw a map of your local area.

What are the main features?

_____

_____

_____

_____

_____

_____

Who helps us?

 What do these people do? How do they help us?

 Neighbourhood watch _____

_____
_____
_____
_____

 Local priest or imam _____

_____
_____
_____
_____

 Police officer _____

_____
_____
_____
_____

 Youth or community leader _____

_____
_____
_____
_____

 MP _____

_____
_____
_____
_____

The mayor

 Fill in this worksheet about your mayor.

What is the name of
the mayor?

_____

_____

_____

_____

_____

Who helps them
with their job?

_____

_____

_____

_____

_____

What is their job?

_____

_____

_____

_____

What special things
do they wear?

_____

_____

_____

_____

_____

48

(12) The media

Background

In this unit the children start to learn about the role of the media, newspapers, radio, television and the Internet.

Learning Objectives

Activities in this unit will allow children to:
- learn more about the media
- understand how news can be presented
- understand that there are sometimes different points of view.

QCA/Curriculum links: QCA Unit 11 • Worksheet 34 links with English, Design & Technology and ICT • Worksheet 35 links with English, Design & Technology and ICT • Worksheet 36 links with English, ICT and Geography.

ACTIVITIES

Worksheet 34 In the news

Starting points: Look through several local newspapers and cut out articles based on one theme, e.g. sport, animals, school events.

Main activity: The children should complete the different ways of broadcasting the news, and write a sentence for five of them.

Simplified activity: Ask the children to draw some of the different ways that the news can be broadcast, e.g. newspaper, radio, television, the Internet, text messaging.

Challenge: The children could look at a selection of national newspapers and pick out a story of interest. They could read it to the rest of the class and say why they found it interesting.

Worksheet 35 Making the news

Starting points: Talk about an event at school. How could this be presented in the media, e.g. as a newspaper article, a radio broadcast or a video?

Main activity: The children should look at the cartoon strip on the worksheet, and write a report for the school newspaper to explain what happened.

Simplified activity: The children could colour in the cartoon strip.

Challenge: Ask the children to imagine that they have to present this story on television. What would they say?

Worksheet 36 Do you agree?

Starting points: Talk to the children about an issue at school, e.g. making breaktimes longer. Ask them to say why it might be a good idea and why it might be a bad idea. Discuss with them the importance of hearing both sides of the argument. Have a discussion about another issues, e.g. whether they should be allowed to bring bicycles to school.

Main activity: The children should read the newspaper article and write down if they agree or disagree with it, giving reasons.

Simplified activity: The children could write down what they would like to add to the newspaper article.

Challenge: In pairs, ask the children to investigate a classroom issue, e.g. whether coats should be allowed in the classroom. They could talk to different members of the class and then write down a selection of opinions.

Plenary

Spend a week producing a class newsletter. This could then be expanded to take in news from throughout the school.

In the news

Complete these media words.

t __ l __ vision   new __ pa __ er

ra __ io   n __ ws

rep __ rt __ r   mag __ z __ ne

Int __ rn __ t   ci __ em __

ar __ icl __   news d __ sk

Now put five of the words into sentences.

1. _____

2. _____

3. _____

4. _____

5. _____

What is the name of your local newspaper? _____

Name two national newspapers. _____

What is the name of your local radio station? _____

Name one news programme on the television. _____

Making the news

Look at the cartoon below.
Write the story for your school newspaper.

Do you agree?

Read this newspaper report.

New road coming soon

A new road is going to be built across Mr Jones's farm. It is being built because there is too much traffic going through the village of Little Woodly. The new road will go past Mr Jones's house and the field where he keeps his cattle. People in the village are pleased that there is going to be a new road.

Mr Jones is worried about the noise of the cars and lorries. He is also worried that the road will have to be crossed when the cows need milking.

Do you think the new road is a good or bad idea? Explain why.

_____

_____

_____

_____

(13) At risk

Background

This unit looks at heath issues. The children will consider how to keep healthy and how to look after their body. They will also learn to identify a number of road signs. They will think about making confident and informed choices about their health and where they live.

Learning Objectives

Activities in this unit will allow children to:
- learn more about a healthy lifestyle
- understand how they can make informed choices
- learn how to behave responsibly on the road.

QCA/Curriculum links: PSHE • Worksheet 37 links with English, Science, Art & Design and PE • Worksheet 38 links with English, Science and Art & Design • Worksheet 39 links with English and Design & Technology.

ACTIVITIES

Worksheet 37 — Looking after our bodies

Starting points: Talk about how we might be able to keep ourselves healthy, concentrating on different forms of exercise. What might the children be able to do after school to keep fit? Why does exercise help?

Main activity: The children should fill in the boxes on the worksheet with a selection of ways to keep healthy, e.g. swimming, running, cycling.

Simplified activity: Ask the children to make a list of physical things that they like to do after school.

Challenge: The children could draw and list some of the things they might find in a gym to help us keep fit. They could go on to design a new piece of equipment.

Worksheet 38 — Being careful

Starting points: Discuss the kind of things that might lead to an unhealthy lifestyle, e.g. smoking, eating too much, not taking enough exercise, drinking too much alcohol.

Main activity: The children should match the pictures with the activities.

Simplified activity: Ask the children to write down what might happen if you drink too much or smoke.

Challenge: The children could design a poster to warn of the dangers of one of the things listed on the worksheet.

Worksheet 39 — On the road

Starting points: Ask the children to consider why road signs are important. Talk about the differences between certain signs such as warning signs (e.g. bend ahead) and order signs (e.g. 40 mph). What might happen if road users do not take any notice of the signs? As a cyclist, why are signs important?

Main activity: The children should look at the road signs and write down what they mean.

Simplified activity: The children could draw a picture and include two or three of the signs.

Challenge: Ask the children to design a set of four new road signs. Write down where and when they would be used. Which one of the signs is the most important and why?

Plenary

Read an extract from Roald Dahl's Charlie and the Chocolate Factory *that describes some of the children who have eaten too much. Talk about why it is a good idea to keep healthy, e.g. less illness, more energy. Discuss what athletes have to do to stay healthy. What happens to people if they get no exercise at all?*

Looking after our bodies

 In the boxes below, draw some of the activities you could do to keep healthy. Write down how they help keep you fit.

_____
_____

_____
_____

_____
_____

_____
_____

How do you like to keep fit and healthy?

_____
_____
_____

Being careful

Match the pictures and the sentences with a line.

You need to get lots of exercise.

Eating too much food is bad for you.

Drinking too much alcohol can damage your body.

Smoking is bad for your health.

Too much sunbathing can cause skin cancer.

On the road

 What do these road signs mean?

Warning signs

Order signs

Order and information signs

Design some road signs of your own.

56

14 Drugs

Background

This unit looks at some of the legal drugs that you can buy and use. It then deals with how illegal drugs can affect people, the need to be responsible and to always say 'no'.

Learning Objectives

Activities in this unit will allow children to:
- learn that some drugs can help you while others can damage you
- understand more about the harm that can be caused by illegal drugs
- learn to say 'no' to all types of dangerous drugs.

QCA/Curriculum links: PSHE • Worksheet 40 links with English and Science • Worksheet 41 links with English and Science • Worksheet 42 links with English, Science and Art & Design.

ACTIVITIES

Worksheet 40 What are drugs?

Starting points: Ask the children to talk about where you might find a selection of medicines, e.g. medicine cabinet, chemist shop. Explain the difference between legal medicines, which help us to get better, and illegal drugs. You could also say that in the USA all medicines are called drugs and that is why you get drug stores. What medicines have the children used to make themselves better? Where are these medicines kept at home?

Main activity: The children should look at the medicines on the worksheet and describe how they can help us. How do medicines help make us better? Which of the things at the bottom of the worksheet might contain drugs and could be dangerous?

Simplified activity: The children could draw some of the things they might have at home in their medicine cabinet.

Challenge: Ask the children to write down any drugs they can think of that are illegal. What might these substances do to people?

Worksheet 41 How do drugs affect us?

Starting points: Discuss how some things that contain drugs can be extremely harmful.

Main activity: The children should consider what kind of things can happen to people who have taken illegal drugs.

Simplified activity: The children could write down three reasons why they should never take drugs.

Challenge: Ask the children to consider what they should do if they spot someone who they think has been taking drugs.

Worksheet 42 Say 'no'

Starting points: Discuss why children should refuse drugs, alcohol and cigarettes. What should they do if someone offers them these things? Who should they tell?

Main activity: The children should write down what they should do if the situation described occurs, listing who they might be able to turn to for help.

Simplified activity: Ask the children to write a list of things that would be dangerous to take or use, e.g. cigarettes, weed killer, glue, alcohol.

Challenge: In small groups, the children could write a short play showing how someone can refuse to take drugs or alcohol.

Plenary

This can be a difficult subject to cover and you may feel that you want to seek further advice from a variety of organisations who work with drug-related issues, e.g.
- *Kidscape (www.kidscape.org.uk)*
- *Re-Solv (www.re-solv.org)*
- *SOLVE IT (www.solveitonline.co.uk)*
- *TACADE (www.tacade.com)*

It is important to discuss the positive side of certain medicines and how they can help cure us.

What are drugs?

How can these drugs help us?

_____

_____

_____

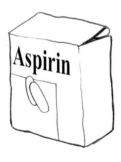

_____

_____

_____

Which of these things containing drugs could be dangerous?
Explain why.

_____ _____ _____

_____ _____ _____

How do drugs affect us?

Underline some of the things that might happen to someone who takes drugs.

1. They get sleepy.

2. They cannot speak properly.

3. Their eyes move strangely.

4. They become angry very quickly.

5. They feel sick.

6. They start to feel very thirsty.

What should you do if you think someone has been taking drugs?

_____

_____

_____

_____

_____

_____

_____

_____

_____

_____

_____

_____

Say 'no'

Read the story below. What would you do if this happened to you?

You are walking home with a friend from school. Three older children come up to you and ask if you would like to go behind the wall and smoke a cigarette.

I would _____

_____

_____

_____

Who would you tell?

1. _____

2. _____

3. _____

Explain why.

_____

_____

_____

_____

_____

60

(15) Bullying

Background

Bullying can take place in and out of school, and it can take many forms: verbal, physical or even silent. Adults can be bullied as well as children. Bullies operate in different ways. They use various methods to 'get' to people, including 'hate' text messages, calling names and physical attack. Bullies like to feel they have power over their victims and keep them quiet.

Learning Objectives

Activities in this unit will allow children to:
- understand what bullying is
- be able to spot someone who is a bully and stand up to them
- know what to do if they are approached by a bully.

QCA/Curriculum links: PSHE • Worksheet 43 links with English • Worksheet 44 links with English • Worksheet 45 links with English.

ACTIVITIES

Worksheet 43 How does bullying work?

Starting points: Ask the children if they can tell you what a bully looks like. It is important to stress that a bully could be anybody. Ask them to list the kind of things a bully might do to frighten their victims. What might a bully do if they are on their own? What might they do if they are in a group?

Main activity: The children should complete the sentences on the sheet, which all deal with bullies.

Simplified activity: Ask the children to draw a picture of a bully.

Challenge: The children could write a story about someone who is being bullied but decides to take action. What happens next?

Worksheet 44 Who are the bullies?

Starting points: People become bullies for different reasons: they may be lonely, they may have been bullied themselves or they may expect everyone to do what they say. Bullies like to be in control and feel powerful. They like it when people are watching them and they are getting what they want. Bullies are found everywhere.

Main activity: The children should tick the sentences which describe why people become bullies.

Simplified activity: Say that bullies often pick on people who are 'different'. Ask the children to write down some of ways in which their friends are different to themselves.

Challenge: Ask the children to write down a list of words that describe a bully and a list that describes the victim.

Worksheet 45 What can you do?

Starting points: Children should know that they can stand up for themselves when faced with a bully. They should be confident and, if possible, walk away from difficult situations. It is best to stay in a group and try not to get angry.

Main activity: The children should look at the people on the worksheet. How can each of them help stop bullying?

Simplified activity: Ask the children to draw an anti-bullying poster.

Challenge: The children could carry out a survey to find out what kind of things cause trouble in the playground. How could breaktimes be made more fun?

Plenary

Discuss how the the children might be able to put on an anti-bullying assembly for the rest of the school. This could include a play, news report, poems and stories. This can be a difficult subject to cover and you may feel that you want to seek further advice from a variety of organisations who work with child-related issues such as Kidscape (www.kidscape.org.uk).

How does bullying work?

Complete these sentences.

1. Bullies look like _____ .

2. Bullies like to get _____ .

3. Name-calling is something _____ .

4. Bullies may hit _____ .

5. Bullies may steal _____ .

6. You may be _____ by a bully.

7. Bullies like to hurt _____ .

8. Bullies sometimes go around in _____ .

9. They like to show how _____ .

10. They sometimes pick on children who are _____ .

Draw a picture of a bully.

Who are the bullies?

Tick the sentences that tell you some of the reasons why people become bullies.

1. They were spoilt as children. ☐

2. There is a lot of fighting at home. ☐

3. They want to be good at sports. ☐

4. They have to be the best at everything. ☐

5. They want to be rich and famous. ☐

6. They can't make any friends. ☐

7. They get bullied at home. ☐

8. Something nasty happened to them. ☐

9. They like to be popular. ☐

10. Their friends are bullies. ☐

Write down two other reasons why people become bullies.

1. _____

_____

2. _____

_____

What can you do?

What can you and these people do to stop bullying?

You

_____
_____
_____

Teacher

_____
_____
_____

Parents

_____
_____
_____

Police

_____
_____
_____
_____

Friends

_____
_____